WAR~ ~~~~
OF H◀

CW00859801

Retold by Brynhildur Thórarinsdóttir

Series Advisor Professor Kimberley Reynolds

Illustrated by Patrick Miller

OXFORD
UNIVERSITY PRESS

Letter from the Author

Imagine a country that does not have any great castles or old ruins; a country where the houses were built of turf, wood and stone and looked like small hills with grass and dandelions growing on the roof; a country that never had its own king or queen and therefore has no palaces or crown jewels. Guess what the national treasure of that country is ... stories!

This country is Iceland, an island that was settled by Vikings[1] in the ninth and tenth centuries. We know a lot about the settlement period because people in Iceland loved to tell stories. They told the stories of their ancestors, and their children retold the stories to their children, and so on and so on, until some people decided to write the old stories on calfskin in the thirteenth century.

The writers did not tell us their names so we do not know who they were.

These stories are called the Icelandic Sagas. They are stories of Vikings – of heroes and fighters, of lovers and rivals, of honour and revenge. Would we know anything about the past if people had not told stories? How close to the truth is a story that has been retold again and again for three hundred years before it is written down? We can only guess. What do you think?

Brynhildur
Thórarinsdóttir

[1] We use the word 'Vikings' to mean Scandinavian raiders and traders who travelled by sea.

GREENLAND

ICELAND

THE JOURNEYS

🚢 ———— EGILL AND THOROLFUR

🚢 ·········· HOSKULDUR

🚢 - - - - - OLAFUR

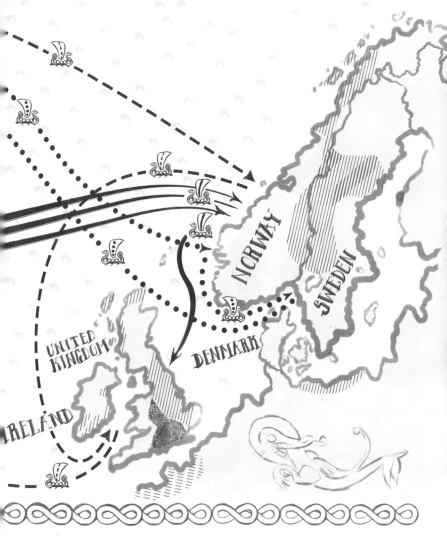

VIKING SETTLEMENTS

▨ 800 - 900 CE

▤ 900 - 1000 CE

▨ 1000 - 1100 CE

Brothers in Arms

From the Saga of Egill Skallagrimsson

More than a thousand years ago, there were two Viking brothers named Egill and Thorolfur. They were among the first children born in Iceland and grew up in a deep fjord[2] on the west coast of Iceland. The older brother, Thorolfur, was tall and handsome and excellent at all sports. He was a pleasant, cheerful boy and very popular.

[2] A fjord is a long, narrow strip of sea, between high cliffs.

Egill was ten years younger than Thorolfur. He was big for his age, and ugly, and he soon became known for his terrible temper. When he was three years old, he was as big and strong as boys of six or seven. He was good with words and enjoyed poetry, but he was also grumpy and mean. Other children were often afraid of him.

When Egill was three years old and Thorolfur thirteen, their grandfather invited their family to a great feast. The parents decided to bring the older boy, but little Egill had to stay behind with his nurse.

Egill was very angry and argued with his father. 'Let me go,' he insisted. 'He is my grandfather as well as Thorolfur's.'

'You will not go,' said his father. 'You are bad enough at home, and you don't know how to behave at these gatherings.'

Little Egill was furious as he watched his parents and his brother Thorolfur ride off to the feast on their horses. He looked at his nurse and he looked at the tired old workhorse his father had once let him ride for fun.

When his nurse was busy, he climbed quietly onto the old horse and rode alone after his parents. He did not know the way, but he sometimes caught a glimpse of his parents between hills and trees.

Late that night, little Egill found his grandfather's farmstead and entered the hall. His thick black hair was ruffled and he was dirty and sweaty from the ride.

The hall was noisy and filled with people sitting on benches alongside long tables.

'Egill!' cried his grandfather. 'Why are you so late?'

'My father did not want me to come,' Egill complained.

'Come sit with me,' his grandfather said and moved on the bench to make space for the little boy.

Egill sat down by his side, across the table from his father and brother. The little boy glared at his father who glared angrily back.

They did not speak. The teenager Thorolfur just rolled his eyes and chatted happily with the other guests.

A longfire[3] was burning in the middle of the hall and the room was hot. Egill drank from a sheep's horn and dug into the huge pile of meat on the table. Soon he was having a great time.

[3] A longfire was a fire that ran the whole length of the room.

Egill listened to the grown-ups talking and laughing and reciting poetry. Nobody noticed him anymore, and he became very annoyed.

'I can make poetry,' little Egill suddenly said loudly.

Everyone stopped talking and stared at the boy. His grandfather roared with laughter. 'Go ahead,' he said.

Egill stepped up on the long table where everyone could see him and made up a poem about his strong and generous grandfather.

Everyone was very impressed and his grandfather cried, 'A great poet must be rewarded!' He handed Egill three beautiful sea shells and a duck's egg as precious toys to play with.

Egill was very pleased, so he stood up and thanked his grandfather with another poem. His brother, Thorolfur, just turned his back.

***

Thorolfur couldn't wait to leave home. As soon as he could, he left Iceland on a Viking ship, looking for fame and fortune abroad. He made friends easily, and he became the best friend of Eirikur Bloodaxe, son of the Norwegian king.

Shortly after they met, the old king died and young Eirikur became king. He made his friend Thorolfur commander of his fleet and together they fought and won many battles.

Thorolfur spent many summers raiding and many winters at the court of Eirikur Bloodaxe in Norway. He became enormously wealthy.

While Thorolfur was abroad, his younger brother Egill got into a lot of trouble. When he was six, he attacked his playmate for beating him at a ball game. But instead of being cross with Egill, his mother was proud of her young warrior. 'One day you will be the captain of your own Viking ship,' she said.

Egill was so pleased that he immediately thought of a poem:

> *My mother she said*
> *I should be bought*
> *a ship with splendid oars.*
> *Sail off with Vikings*
> *bravely in the bow,*
> *Bring the ship to shore.*
> *Swiftly draw my sword,*
> *Slay one after another.*

However, Egill didn't get along with his father. They fought like wolves, and when Egill was twelve years old they did not speak a single word to each other for an entire winter.

The next summer, Thorolfur came back home with all his silver and glory. He spent the winter at his parents' farmstead, but in the spring he prepared to sail back to Norway. When Thorolfur's ship was ready, Egill approached him. 'I want to go with you,' he said.

Thorolfur refused and said, 'You are bad enough at home and it is impossible for me to look after you abroad.'

'Then neither of us is going,' Egill responded angrily.

That night, Egill sneaked out and cut his brother's ship loose with an axe. It drifted across the fjord and became stranded.

Thorolfur was very angry but his younger brother was even angrier.

'I will do worse things if you don't take me with you,' Egill threatened.

Finally, Thorolfur gave up. 'All right, you can come with me to Norway,' he sighed.

Thorolfur introduced his brother to his friends in Norway, but Egill got into all sorts of trouble with rich and powerful people. His behaviour was impossible everywhere – except on the battlefield.

One day, Thorolfur approached his brother. 'You should come on a Viking raid with me,' he said to him. Egill smiled. They sailed on Thorolfur's Viking ship, raided and ransacked, and collected a huge amount of silver and treasures. In battle, the two very different brothers discovered that they had more in common than they thought. They became inseparable friends.

Once, the brothers heard that King Athelstan of England was hiring warriors. The King of Scotland had taken Northumberland and King Athelstan was in great need of a bigger army. Thorolfur and Egill sailed to England with three hundred warriors and joined the army of King Athelstan.

King Athelstan counted on his Viking warriors. He split up his army and made Egill and Thorolfur commanders of the two separate battalions.

The Scottish army was enormous and the battle was fierce. The Scots attacked Thorolfur and his battalion but Thorolfur fought back heroically. And yet, he could not escape all the spears.

When Egill heard of his brother's death he went into a frenzy of rage. He led his battalion into battle and fought ferociously until the Scottish army had been defeated.

King Athelstan had won! To celebrate this important victory, he invited his supporters and friends to a great feast.

Meanwhile Egill took care of his brother's body and buried him with his weapons, according to Viking custom. He then hurried to the victory feast.

Egill threw the great doors open and marched furiously into the hall in full armour, still dirty and sweaty from the battlefield. He was a huge man with broad shoulders, his eyes were fiery and from underneath his helmet flowed his long, wolf-grey hair. The feast grew silent.

'Egill!' cried King Athelstan. 'Welcome!'

Egill did not respond.

'Have a seat,' said the King, and ordered some guests to move from the seat of honour opposite his throne.

Egill sat down with his shield at his feet. He was still wearing his helmet and clenched his sword, dragging it partway out of the sheath and then slamming it back in.

He was deeply upset.

King Athelstan sat quietly on his
throne for a while.

Then the King took a large band of gold
from his arm and placed it on the tip of his
sword. He walked across the floor and offered
the ring to Egill over the longfire.

Egill stood up and approached the King.
He reached over the fire and caught the ring
by the tip of his sword.

Egill returned to his seat and put the golden band on his arm. He considered the King on his throne. Neither man said a single word. He considered the proof of the King's appreciation on his arm and a warm smile lit up his face.

'And now,' he said, 'a poem about our victory and my reward.'

The Death of a Hero
From the Saga of Njall

Hallgerdur was a young Viking girl in the western part of Iceland. She was tall for her age and very beautiful. Her father was very proud of her. Once, at a feast, she was playing on the floor with a group of children. Her father pointed his daughter out to his brother.

'Isn't she lovely?' he asked.

'Indeed she is a very beautiful girl,' answered his brother, who was a wise and respected man. 'Her beauty will cause much suffering. But she has the eyes of a thief!'

Hallgerdur's father got very angry and did not speak to his brother for a long time. But her uncle's predictions eventually came true.

Hallgerdur grew up to be the most beautiful woman of her time. Because of her height she was called Hallgerdur Langbrok, which means 'long legs'. Her hair was soft as silk and long enough for her to wrap it around her body. Her temper was, however, short and she took orders from nobody.

By the time she was seventeen, her father had twice made her marry someone she did not choose. Both husbands treated her badly and both husbands died violently because of her. The very young widow was left with a daughter and plenty of money.

Hallgerdur did not marry again for many years. But one summer night, she met the man of her dreams. Gunnar was young and strong, rich and handsome, polite and charming, and he dressed like a king. He was able to jump his full height head over heels in full armour, backward as well as forward. He swam like a seal, was successful at all sports, and he never missed his mark once he had taken aim. People said that he had no equals in the land.

Hallgerdur immediately fell in love with this great warrior and he fell for this beautiful older woman. His friends warned him against her, but they soon married and she moved to his farmstead, Hlidarendi.

Gunnar was a popular man who enjoyed holding feasts for his many friends. One cold year, the harvest failed throughout the land. There was little food and many people were hungry the following winter.

Hallgerdur worried that there would not be enough to eat at Hlidarendi, and she asked her husband to buy some food from their neighbour, Otkell.

But Otkell refused to sell his food, even though he had plenty left. Instead, he tricked Gunnar into buying a lazy and unpopular Celtic slave.

Hallgerdur was very upset when Gunnar came home with an unwanted slave but no food. It was her responsibility to ensure the household could be fed throughout the year.

Even though they had so little food left, Gunnar decided to invite his friends for an overnight feast. Hallgerdur had to prepare the feast. She called the unwanted slave. 'Go to Otkell's farmstead and load two horses with food from his barn,' she ordered him. 'Then burn down the barn, so nobody will find out.'

The slave followed her orders. Hallgerdur then served the stolen food at the feast.

Gunnar was astonished to see the fine food his wife served the guests, and asked where it came from.

'Mind your own business,' she replied. 'The preparation of food is no concern of men.'

Gunnar became very angry. 'I will not be the partner of a thief,' he said, and slapped her across the face.

Hallgerdur was furious. 'I will remember that slap,' she shouted, 'and pay you back when I can.'

The next months were not peaceful. Gunnar offered Otkell compensation for his destroyed barn but Otkell refused.

One day, Gunnar was sowing grain when Otkell came galloping straight at him and accidentally hurt Gunnar's face.

After that, Otkell boasted whenever he could, 'Did you hear that Gunnar wept when I rode at him?'

Gunnar was deeply offended. Vikings did not cry! At the first opportunity, he and his brother, Kolskeggur, ambushed Otkell, along with seven of his men.

A fierce battle broke out, and in the end Gunnar and Kolskeggur killed Otkell and all his companions.

The friends of Gunnar feared that the families of the men he had killed would take revenge. His brother-in-law warned him to be careful, and gave him an Irish wolfhound named Samur.

'Samur is as clever as a human,' he said. 'He will bark at anyone he knows to be your enemy, but he will never bark at your friends. He will give his life to be loyal to you'.

The dog followed Gunnar wherever he went and guarded Hlidarendi every night. As autumn drew near, the conflict flared up again. Following another battle, Gunnar and Kolskeggur were outlawed at the Althingi assembly.[4] They had to go abroad for three years or their enemies could legally kill them.

[4] The Althingi was a general assembly that served as both a parliament and a court.

A ship awaited the brothers by the coast.
Gunnar had their belongings brought to the
ship and said goodbye to Hallgerdur and their
two sons. Then he rode off with Kolskeggur.

When they came to the river, Gunnar's
horse stumbled and he was forced to leap
from the saddle. Gunnar looked up towards
his homestead and he knew he had to meet
his fate. 'Beautiful is the hillside,' he said.

'The fields are bright and the pastures green. I will not leave, but return home forever.'

'Do not ignore the outlaw sentence!' Kolskeggur warned him. 'Our ship and our freedom are near!'

'I am not leaving, and I wish you would stay as well,' Gunnar replied.

'Then we will part,' Kolskeggur said sadly. 'Tell our mother I am not coming back to Iceland because you will be dead.'

Kolskeggur rode to the ship but Gunnar went home to Hlidarendi. Hallgerdur was glad to see him, but his mother kept quiet, worrying what would happen to him.

The news that Gunnar had not sailed soon reached his enemies. One autumn night, a group of armed men gathered and rode towards Hlidarendi. They knew they would have to take Gunnar by surprise if they were to defeat him. That meant they had to get rid of Samur. Under the threat of death, they forced Gunnar's neighbour to distract the dog.

When Samur saw Gunnar's friend approaching he did not bark, but ran happily to greet him. One of the attackers killed the dog with his battle axe. The howling of the dog as it died awoke Gunnar.

'Goodbye my friend Samur,' he said. 'My enemies have been cruel to you. No doubt I will follow you shortly.' Gunnar then collected his weapons and took position at one of the windows.

The men surrounded the house. Gunnar had his bow and quiver of arrows and defended himself well. He drew one arrow after another and it was impossible to get to him.

Finally, one of his enemies managed to run up the wall with his sword and cut the string of Gunnar's bow. Gunnar immediately killed

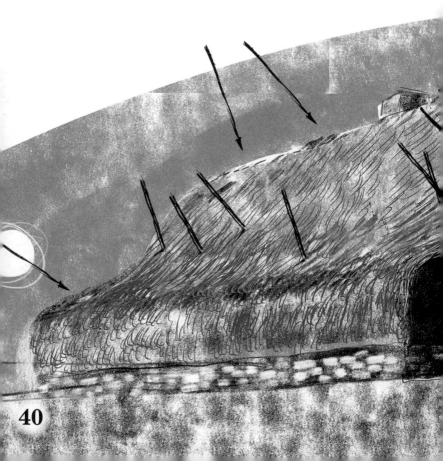

the man with his spear. He was wounded, but he had now wounded eight of his enemies and killed two.

Gunnar turned to his wife. 'Hallgerdur,' he said, 'cut off some of your hair and twist it to make a new string for my bow.'

'Why do you want me to do that?' asked Hallgerdur.

'My life is at stake!' said Gunnar. 'But they will never defeat me as long as I can use my bow.'

'I haven't forgotten how you slapped me,' said Hallgerdur. 'I don't see why I should interfere in your battle.'

'Very well,' said Gunnar. 'I will not ask you again.'

This was the last time they spoke to each other. Gunnar continued to defend himself with great courage, and wounded eight more men. In the end, however, his enemies killed him.

The bad news of Gunnar's death travelled quickly throughout the land and his heroic story was told and retold for a thousand years.

Hallgerdur lived a long life, but she never married again.

The Slave Princess
From Laxdaela Saga

Hoskuldur was a respected Viking chieftain in western Iceland. Like all chieftains, he often sailed to Scandinavia to trade. One year, he attended a famous summer fair in Sweden.

Hoskuldur walked around the fair where merchants from all the Viking territories had put up their tents. He had a bag of silver at his waist and a ship full of supplies and presents to take home to his wife, Jorunn, and their four children. Yet he was curious to see what the traders had to offer.

Hoskuldur passed a decorated tent. It was attended by a strangely-dressed man in a large fur hat. When Hoskuldur looked in his tent he saw a group of slaves sitting in a row. At the back he saw a beautiful, poorly-dressed young woman trying to hide herself. Hoskuldur could not take his eyes off her.

The slave-seller saw
where he was looking.
'I have to warn you,'
he said. 'This one
is deaf and she
cannot speak.'

'I don't mind,'
Hoskuldur said
and counted
his silver.

Hoskuldur gave the young woman lovely clothes and threw away her slave-dress. 'You look astonishing,' he said.

She did not respond.

'I'm taking you with me to Iceland,' he said. 'You will like it there.'

'Do you have a name?' he asked. 'Where are you from?'

The slave never answered.

Hoskuldur sailed to Iceland and introduced the young woman to his family. Jorunn was not impressed by the new member of the household, but everyone else admired her grace and beauty.

After a while, Hoskuldur and the young slave had a son. Hoskuldur loved the boy dearly and named him Olafur. The boy's mother did not say if she liked the name; she never spoke at all.

When the boy was two winters old, he could speak perfectly and ran around on his own like a child of four. He was a beautiful little boy who looked a lot like his mother.

One morning Hoskuldur rose early to work. He heard voices coming from a creek at the edge of the field. When he came closer, he saw that little Olafur and his mother were talking.

'Mother, tell me a story,' the boy begged.

'Of course, my darling,' his mother said. 'What story would you like to hear?'

The boy giggled. 'The one you always tell me: the one with the king.'

His mother hugged him. 'That is my favourite story as well. Once upon a time …'

Hoskuldur was amazed. He approached the woman he had thought was deaf and mute. 'You cannot hide anymore,' he said. 'What is your name?'

49

She paused for a moment before answering. 'If you care about my name, I can tell you it is Melkorka.'

'Tell me about yourself, Melkorka,' Hoskuldur asked. 'Where are you from?'

'My father is named Myrkjartan,' she said. 'He is a king in Ireland. I was captured there and enslaved when I was fifteen years old.'

'You have long kept silent about such a noble family!' Hoskuldur said. He was so excited about this discovery that he ran inside shouting to his wife, 'The slave-woman is not mute! She is an Irish princess!'

Jorunn was not impressed. 'Does she say that? You will never know if she is telling the truth,' she remarked.

Olafur grew up to be a handsome, strong and well-mannered young man. As a twelve-year-old, he behaved like a grown-up chieftain. He liked to dress well in colourful clothes, and to carry shining weapons.

'You are like a peacock,' his father remarked.

After that the boy became known as Olafur Peacock.

When Olafur Peacock was still quite young, his mother said, 'I want you to go to Ireland and meet your noble kinsmen. As I have told you, the King of Ireland is your grandfather.'

'My father does not want me to go,' Olafur responded.

'Don't worry about that,' Melkorka said. 'I do not want people calling you the son of a slave. I will find a way.'

Melkorka was clever, and she got a rich chieftain to take Olafur on his ship to Norway. From there, she felt sure he would be able to use his ingenuity to get to Ireland. Before the boy left, she spoke to him in private. She gave him a large golden ring and said, 'My father gave me this ring. He will recognize it.'

Then she handed him a knife and a belt. 'Give these things to my old nurse,' she said. 'She will recognize them.'

Finally she hugged him. 'I have given you all you need, and I have taught you to speak such good Irish that you will be able to speak to people anywhere in Ireland.'

Olafur thanked his mother and boarded the ship. He sailed with the chieftain to Norway where they visited the King. The King was a good friend of Hoskuldur and he invited Olafur to stay at the court for the winter. Olafur proved himself to be a great addition to the court. But when spring came, Olafur became restless.

'What is the matter?' asked the old Queen.

She was especially fond of this young chivalrous Icelander.

'I want to go to Ireland,' Olafur said, 'to meet my grandfather, a king in Ireland.'

The Queen was surprised, yet she had a ship prepared for him and manned it with warriors. 'The ship is yours,' she said.

At the age of eighteen, Olafur was now the captain of a Viking ship and the commander of sixty warriors.

Olafur sailed to Ireland, but in the dark of night, his ship became stuck in mud close to the shore. Soon, many Irish people arrived at the coast. The Irish had suffered for years at the hands of Viking raiders, and they assumed Olafur had come to plunder their land like all the others. They were keen to get their revenge.

'Everything on board a stranded ship belongs to us,' someone shouted. 'This is the Irish law.'

'The ship is not stranded,' Olafur argued in Irish. 'It is merely stuck at low tide.'

'Drag the ship ashore!' The Irish gave a war cry and charged into the sea.

'Form a wall of shields,' Olafur ordered his men. Immediately they all lifted their shields, and stuck their spears out below them.

Olafur Peacock stepped up into the bow of the ship, wearing full armour and a golden-red helmet. His sword had golden hilts and a golden lion decorated his red shield.

The Irish retreated. 'This is no ordinary merchant ship,' someone shouted. 'This is a warship! Someone must warn the King!'

Soon a company of well-armed horsemen approached, led by King Myrkjartan himself. 'Who are you and where do you come from?' the King demanded.

'My name is Olafur,' answered Olafur Peacock. 'However, I expect you know more than I about my mother's kinsmen. Her name is Melkorka and she is your daughter.'

The King fell silent for a while. Finally he said, 'Come ashore. We need to discuss the matter further.'

Olafur came ashore, removed his helmet, and knelt before the King.

He told his full story and presented the King
with the ring that Melkorka had
given him in Iceland.

The King examined the
ring and his face went very
red. Then he said, 'I recognize
this ring, but I also recognize
my daughter in you.'

King Myrkjartan rode to Dublin with
his grandson and the news caused much
amazement throughout Ireland.

Melkorka's old nurse was sick, but she came
to greet them. Olafur gave her his mother's
knife and belt and the nurse's eyes filled with
tears of joy as she recognized them.

Olafur and his men spent the winter with
the King, defending Ireland from raiders.
Olafur proved himself to be a clever and
courageous commander, and in
spring the King addressed the
great assembly.

'I would like Olafur to become king after my day, since he is a better leader than any of my sons,' he announced.

Olafur chose his words very carefully. 'I do not want to fight your sons when you die,' he said. 'It is better to enjoy brief honour than extended shame.'

Olafur praised the King, but added, 'I want to return home to my mother as soon as weather permits.'

So the King accompanied Olafur to his ship and gave him decorated weapons and many other treasures. They parted in great friendship.

Olafur returned home to his mother, and eventually became one of the greatest chieftains of Iceland.